Kilmann Organizational Conflict Instrument

D1616092

RALPH H. KILMANN

CO-CREATOR OF THE THOMAS-KILMANN
CONFICT MODE INSTRUMENT (TKI)

More than 8,000,000 copies sold

Distributed by
KILMANN DIAGNOSTICS LLC
1 Suprema Drive
Newport Coast, CA 92657
www.kilmanndiagnostics.com
info@kilmanndiagnostics.com
949.497.8766

Introduction and Overview

How well do your needs and interests fit with your organization's goals and procedures? Asked a bit differently, are you in alignment with your organization or...do you often find yourself at odds—in conflict—with what your organization expects from you?

This assessment tool reveals the "systems conflicts" that exist between you and your organization, which include both the formal and informal systems, as well as the processes and procedures that take place within those systems. And just how these individual/organizational differences are resolved not only determines your performance and satisfaction, but also determines the survival and success of your organization.

In **PART 1,** you are first asked to indicate how often you experience the negative effects from a variety of systems conflicts in your organization.

In **PART 2**, you're asked to indicate the relative frequency that you use different conflict-handling modes to address those systems conflicts.

"I must create a system, or be enslaved by another man's."
William Blake, poet, circa 1800

KILMANN ORGANIZATIONAL CONFLICT INSTRUMENT

Part 1: Instructions

Below are 27 typical "systems conflicts" that take place in organizations. On the five-point scale for each item, *please indicate how often you are negatively affected by that particular conflict* by circling the relevant number: **1 = *Never*, 2 = *Rarely*, 3 = *Occasionally*, 4 = *Frequently*, or 5 = *Always.*** Be sure to keep the same organization or work group clearly in mind as you respond to each and every item.

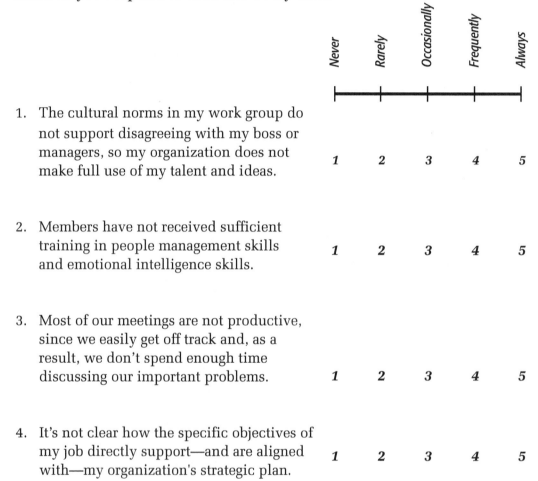

	Never	Rarely	Occasionally	Frequently	Always
1. The cultural norms in my work group do not support disagreeing with my boss or managers, so my organization does not make full use of my talent and ideas.	1	2	3	4	5
2. Members have not received sufficient training in people management skills and emotional intelligence skills.	1	2	3	4	5
3. Most of our meetings are not productive, since we easily get off track and, as a result, we don't spend enough time discussing our important problems.	1	2	3	4	5
4. It's not clear how the specific objectives of my job directly support—and are aligned with—my organization's strategic plan.	1	2	3	4	5

KILMANN ORGANIZATIONAL CONFLICT INSTRUMENT

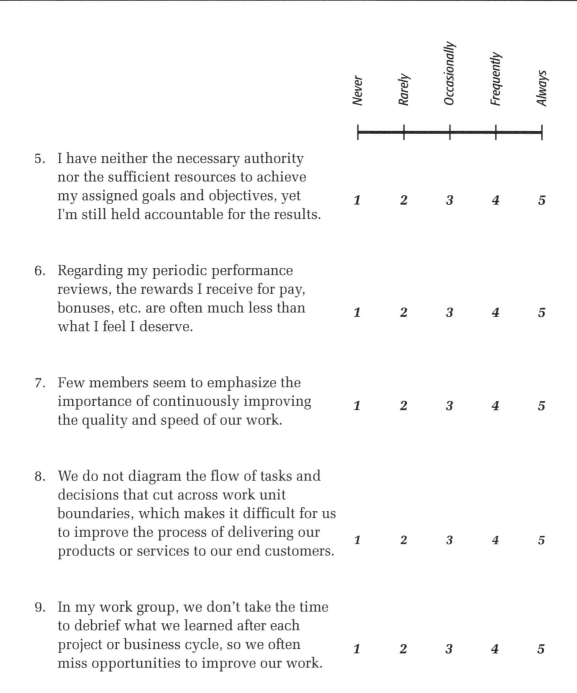

	Never	Rarely	Occasionally	Frequently	Always
5. I have neither the necessary authority nor the sufficient resources to achieve my assigned goals and objectives, yet I'm still held accountable for the results.	1	2	3	4	5
6. Regarding my periodic performance reviews, the rewards I receive for pay, bonuses, etc. are often much less than what I feel I deserve.	1	2	3	4	5
7. Few members seem to emphasize the importance of continuously improving the quality and speed of our work.	1	2	3	4	5
8. We do not diagram the flow of tasks and decisions that cut across work unit boundaries, which makes it difficult for us to improve the process of delivering our products or services to our end customers.	1	2	3	4	5
9. In my work group, we don't take the time to debrief what we learned after each project or business cycle, so we often miss opportunities to improve our work.	1	2	3	4	5

KILMANN ORGANIZATIONAL CONFLICT INSTRUMENT

	Never	Rarely	Occasionally	Frequently	Always
10. It's best to keep new ideas and radically different perspectives to yourself, rather than risk the criticism of other group members, let alone being put down by your boss or other senior managers.	1	2	3	4	5
11. Members have not received sufficient training in handling conflicts, since we continually face the same conflicts without reaching satisfying solutions.	1	2	3	4	5
12. The boss does most of the talking during our meetings, without actively soliciting the valuable ideas from members.	1	2	3	4	5
13. My organization has a mission statement, but it neither engages my enthusiasm nor helps me prioritize my daily work.	1	2	3	4	5
14. There's too much bureaucracy in this organization, which makes it difficult to get timely guidance or decisions so I can perform my best work on time.	1	2	3	4	5
15. My boss and/or group members do not express their appreciation for what I have contributed to this organization.	1	2	3	4	5

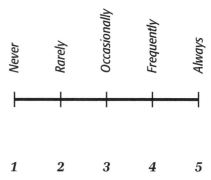

16. The members in my group each have their own way of getting the work done, so the customer tends to receive different services, depending on who handled the issue on a particular day or time.

   1   2   3   4   5

17. Our departments are not designed around the key business processes that matter most to our customers, which results in much wasted time and effort by having to continually move inputs and outputs across our highly specialized areas.

   1   2   3   4   5

18. We don't have a database that captures and stores our best practices for managing complex projects, so we have to keep "reinventing the wheel" every time a new project is initiated.

   1   2   3   4   5

19. We tend to look the other way if we see a boss or manager mistreat subordinates (or women and minorities), since it's not wise to confront a manager's bad behavior.

   1   2   3   4   5

20. Members have not received sufficient training in time management skills, so we can't complete our highest priority tasks in the shortest amount of time.

   1   2   3   4   5

KILMANN ORGANIZATIONAL CONFLICT INSTRUMENT

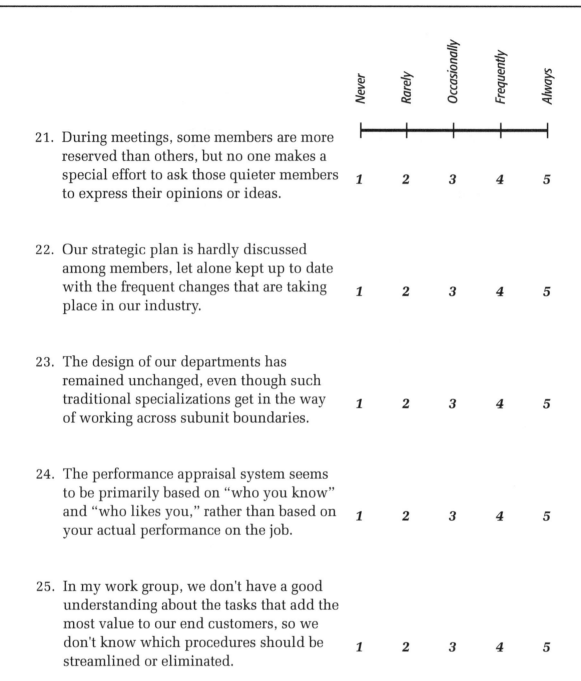

	Never	Rarely	Occasionally	Frequently	Always
21. During meetings, some members are more reserved than others, but no one makes a special effort to ask those quieter members to express their opinions or ideas.	1	2	3	4	5
22. Our strategic plan is hardly discussed among members, let alone kept up to date with the frequent changes that are taking place in our industry.	1	2	3	4	5
23. The design of our departments has remained unchanged, even though such traditional specializations get in the way of working across subunit boundaries.	1	2	3	4	5
24. The performance appraisal system seems to be primarily based on "who you know" and "who likes you," rather than based on your actual performance on the job.	1	2	3	4	5
25. In my work group, we don't have a good understanding about the tasks that add the most value to our end customers, so we don't know which procedures should be streamlined or eliminated.	1	2	3	4	5

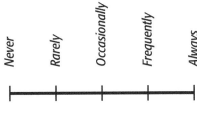

26. In my organizations, we have rigid boundaries between our departments (also called empires or fiefdoms), which makes it exceedingly difficult to have effective cross-functional teams and project groups that consist of members who represent those different specializations.

1   2   3   4   5

27. Much of the vital knowledge in my organization remains in the minds and memories of key individuals, so if they leave, we won't have an accessible database for retrieving the best ways to manage complex problems and projects.

1   2   3   4   5

Part 2: Instructions

Below are nine summary descriptions of each of the major categories of systems conflicts in organizations—which are based on the eight tracks (culture, skills, teams, strategy-structure, rewards, gradual process, radical process, and learning process). In Part 1 of this instrument, you revealed how often you have experienced the negative effects of these conflicts in your organization. For Part 2, you are now asked to indicate how you try to resolve each of those major categories of systems conflicts, according to *five different conflict-handling modes.*

Specifically, for each category of systems conflict (numbered 28 to 36), indicate your relative use of the five conflict-handling modes—starting from the highest number "5" (for the most used conflict mode), to "4" (the next used conflict mode), and so on, all the way down to "1" (the least used conflict mode). *Be sure to distinguish your relative use of the conflict modes by always assigning all five numbers (5, 4, 3, 2, 1) to those five different approaches to conflict for each of the nine systems conflicts.* As you did before, keep the same organization or work group clearly in mind as you respond to Part 2 of this instrument.

28. How are you likely to respond when you experience the negative aspects of the **CULTURE** in your organization—regarding the unwritten norms that suggest how you should behave inside your group (including your behavior toward your boss) and how you're supposed to behave toward others who are outside your group?

    Be sure to assign all five numbers: _5_ = most used conflict mode, _4_ = next used conflict mode, _3_ = the next used conflict mode, _2_ = the next to last used mode, and _1_ = the least used mode.

A ___ Sometimes, it's simply not worth the extra time and effort it would take to discuss and examine this particular aspect of the organization, since we're unlikely to find a good solution.

B ___ I prefer to let other members examine this particular aspect of the organization, since others are often more affected by these issues, and know more about this situation than I do.

C ___ I always ask my boss or team members to take the necessary time to thoroughly discuss this particular aspect of the organization, so we can develop a creative solution for everyone's benefit.

D ___ It's easy to propose a quick, middle-ground, workable solution to this particular aspect of the organization, so we don't waste a lot of time and effort digging deeply into such difficult issues.

E ___ I usually let my boss and other members know exactly how I feel (and what I believe) about this particular aspect of our organization, whenever it affects or frustrates me in any way.

29. How are you likely to respond when you experience the negative aspects of the **SKILLS** in your organization—regarding the use of people management skills, emotional intelligence skills, how complex problems are defined and resolved both inside and outside your work group, and whether time is being managed efficiently according to agreed-upon goals and objectives?

   Be sure to assign all five numbers: _5_ = most used conflict mode, _4_ = next used conflict mode, _3_ = the next used conflict mode, _2_ = the next to last used mode, and _1_ = the least used mode.

A ___ Sometimes, it's simply not worth the extra time and effort it would take to discuss and examine this particular aspect of the organization, since we're unlikely to find a good solution.

B ___ I prefer to let other members examine this particular aspect of the organization, since others are often more affected by these issues, and know more about this situation than I do.

C ___ I always ask my boss or team members to take the necessary time to thoroughly discuss this particular aspect of the organization, so we can develop a creative solution for everyone's benefit.

D ___ It's easy to propose a quick, middle-ground, workable solution to this particular aspect of the organization, so we don't waste a lot of time and effort digging deeply into such difficult issues.

E ___ I usually let my boss and other members know exactly how I feel (and what I believe) about this particular aspect of our organization, whenever it affects or frustrates me in any way.

30 How are you likely to respond when you experience the negative aspects of the **TEAMS** in your organization—regarding how group meetings are conducted, whether the group discusses topics in the order of their priority, whether the quieter members of the group are explicitly drawn into the discussion, and whether the boss makes sure that all the wisdom and experience in the group is brought to bear on its major responsibilities, tasks and decisions?

(5 = most used conflict mode, 4 = next used conflict mode, etc.)

A ___ Sometimes, it's simply not worth the extra time and effort it would take to discuss and examine this particular aspect of the organization, since we're unlikely to find a good solution.

B ___ I prefer to let other members examine this particular aspect of the organization, since others are often more affected by these issues, and know more about this situation than I do.

C ___ I always ask my boss or team members to take the necessary time to thoroughly discuss this particular aspect of the organization, so we can develop a creative solution for everyone's benefit.

D ___ It's easy to propose a quick, middle-ground, workable solution to this particular aspect of the organization, so we don't waste a lot of time and effort digging deeply into such difficult issues.

E ___ I usually let my boss and other members know exactly how I feel (and what I believe) about this particular aspect of our organization, whenever it affects or frustrates me in any way.

31. How are you likely to respond when you experience the negative aspects of your organization's **STRATEGY**—regarding whether the mission statement is well-written, up-to-date, passionate, and known throughout the organization, including whether a long-term strategic plan has been developed and translated into short-term goals and objectives, which are then further translated into clear responsibilities for each work group and job in the organization?

(_5_ = most used conflict mode, _4_ = next used conflict mode, etc.)

A ___   Sometimes, it's simply not worth the extra time and effort it would take to discuss and examine this particular aspect of the organization, since we're unlikely to find a good solution.

B ___   I prefer to let other members examine this particular aspect of the organization, since others are often more affected by these issues, and know more about this situation than I do.

C ___   I always ask my boss or team members to take the necessary time to thoroughly discuss this particular aspect of the organization, so we can develop a creative solution for everyone's benefit.

D ___   It's easy to propose a quick, middle-ground, workable solution to this particular aspect of the organization, so we don't waste a lot of time and effort digging deeply into such difficult issues.

E ___   I usually let my boss and other members know exactly how I feel (and what I believe) about this particular aspect of our organization, whenever it affects or frustrates me in any way.

32. How are you likely to respond when you experience the negative aspects of your organization's **STRUCTURE**—regarding how well short-term objectives and tasks have been arranged into well-defined departments and work groups, which affects whether members have the necessary authority and resources to complete their assigned jobs within their primary work unit to the best of their ability, including the efficiency of the management hierarchy that's needed to coordinate the processes that still flow across departmental or work unit boundaries?

(5 = most used conflict mode, 4 = next used conflict mode, etc.)

A ___ Sometimes, it's simply not worth the extra time and effort it would take to discuss and examine this particular aspect of the organization, since we're unlikely to find a good solution.

B ___ I prefer to let other members examine this particular aspect of the organization, since others are often more affected by these issues, and know more about this situation than I do.

C ___ I always ask my boss or team members to take the necessary time to thoroughly discuss this particular aspect of the organization, so we can develop a creative solution for everyone's benefit.

D ___ It's easy to propose a quick, middle-ground, workable solution to this particular aspect of the organization, so we don't waste a lot of time and effort digging deeply into such difficult issues.

E ___ I usually let my boss and other members know exactly how I feel (and what I believe) about this particular aspect of our organization, whenever it affects or frustrates me in any way.

33. How are you likely to respond when you experience the negative aspects of your organization's **REWARDS**—regarding the design and functioning of the performance appraisal system, whether the performance criteria reflect the current objectives of the job holder, whether the relevant performance criteria are applied accurately and fairly for all members, and whether helpful and supportive feedback discussions take place that enable members to improve their behavior and results during the next performance cycle?

(_5_ = most used conflict mode, _4_ = next used conflict mode, etc.)

A ___ Sometimes, it's simply not worth the extra time and effort it would take to discuss and examine this particular aspect of the organization, since we're unlikely to find a good solution.

B ___ I prefer to let other members examine this particular aspect of the organization, since others are often more affected by these issues, and know more about this situation than I do.

C ___ I always ask my boss or team members to take the necessary time to thoroughly discuss this particular aspect of the organization, so we can develop a creative solution for everyone's benefit.

D ___ It's easy to propose a quick, middle-ground, workable solution to this particular aspect of the organization, so we don't waste a lot of time and effort digging deeply into such difficult issues.

E ___ I usually let my boss and other members know exactly how I feel (and what I believe) about this particular aspect of our organization, whenever it affects or frustrates me in any way.

34. How are you likely to respond when you experience the negative aspects of **PROCESS** management that take place within work groups (known as **GRADUAL** process improvement)—regarding whether group members diagram the flow of their major tasks and decisions, so they can eliminate unnecessary steps and thus streamline, control, and then improve the quality of their work for the benefit of their end customers and other key stakeholders?

(5 = most used conflict mode, 4 = next used conflict mode, etc.)

A ___ Sometimes, it's simply not worth the extra time and effort it would take to discuss and examine this particular aspect of the organization, since we're unlikely to find a good solution.

B ___ I prefer to let other members examine this particular aspect of the organization, since others are often more affected by these issues, and know more about this situation than I do.

C ___ I always ask my boss or team members to take the necessary time to thoroughly discuss this particular aspect of the organization, so we can develop a creative solution for everyone's benefit.

D ___ It's easy to propose a quick, middle-ground, workable solution to this particular aspect of the organization, so we don't waste a lot of time and effort digging deeply into such difficult issues.

E ___ I usually let my boss and other members know exactly how I feel (and what I believe) about this particular aspect of our organization, whenever it affects or frustrates me in any way.

35. How are you likely to respond when you experience the negative aspects of **PROCESS** management that cut across existing work unit boundaries (known as **RADICAL** process improvement)—regarding whether cross-functional teams take the time to manage the tasks and decisions that flow across their respective work units, so they can streamline, control, and then improve the quality of their cross-boundary business processes for the benefit of their end customers and other key stakeholders?

(5 = most used conflict mode, 4 = next used conflict mode, etc.)

A ___ Sometimes, it's simply not worth the extra time and effort it would take to discuss and examine this particular aspect of the organization, since we're unlikely to find a good solution.

B ___ I prefer to let other members examine this particular aspect of the organization, since others are often more affected by these issues, and know more about this situation than I do.

C ___ I always ask my boss or team members to take the necessary time to thoroughly discuss this particular aspect of the organization, so we can develop a creative solution for everyone's benefit.

D ___ It's easy to propose a quick, middle-ground, workable solution to this particular aspect of the organization, so we don't waste a lot of time and effort digging deeply into such difficult issues.

E ___ I usually let my boss and other members know exactly how I feel (and what I believe) about this particular aspect of our organization, whenever it affects or frustrates me in any way.

36. How are you likely to respond when you experience the negative aspects of **PROCESS** management that considers how well the organization learns from its prior achievements and challenges (known as **LEARNING** process improvement)—regarding whether the knowledge of best practices within the organization (and benchmarking how other organizations have managed those same kinds of challenges) are captured, stored in databases, shared among work units, and then used effectively, so members don't have to "reinvent the wheel" and learn everything from scratch?

(5 = most used conflict mode, 4 = next used conflict mode, etc.)

A ___ Sometimes, it's simply not worth the extra time and effort it would take to discuss and examine this particular aspect of the organization, since we're unlikely to find a good solution.

B ___ I prefer to let other members examine this particular aspect of the organization, since others are often more affected by these issues, and know more about this situation than I do.

C ___ I always ask my boss or team members to take the necessary time to thoroughly discuss this particular aspect of the organization, so we can develop a creative solution for everyone's benefit.

D ___ It's easy to propose a quick, middle-ground, workable solution to this particular aspect of the organization, so we don't waste a lot of time and effort digging deeply into such difficult issues.

E ___ I usually let my boss and other members know exactly how I feel (and what I believe) about this particular aspect of our organization, whenever it affects or frustrates me in any way.

Scoring Your Responses to Part 1

In the spaces next to the items on the following page, please transfer the numbers you circled on Part 1 of this instrument. You will find it easiest to transfer your responses in sequence from item Number 1 through item Number 27. It is essential that you transfer every number accurately.

Next, separately add up each of the 9 columns, which results in **9 SUMS.** These SUMS constitute your Part 1 scores for 9 systems conflicts.

Although you responded to nine varieties of systems conflicts (culture, skills, teams, strategy, structure, rewards, gradual process, radical process, and learning process), it is most useful to *combine* strategy and structure into one average score: **strategy-structure.** Strategy is a formal statement of "where we are headed," while structure shows the formal arrangement of authority and resources into subunits and a management hierarchy for "how we are organized to get there." For the purpose of improvement and transformation, it's best to consider "strategy-structure" as one combined formal system, since structure must be designed to implement strategy.

As suggested on the following page, add up your **2 SUMS** for strategy and structure, **divide by 2,** and then place this AVERAGE score into the box: **Strategy-Structure.**

In a short while, you'll be able to graph your results from Part 1 and also combine them with your results from Part 2 of this instrument.

KILMANN ORGANIZATIONAL CONFLICT INSTRUMENT

Culture

1. ____
10. ____
19. ____

Skills

2. ____
11. ____
20. ____

Teams

3. ____
12. ____
21. ____

Strategy

4. ____
13. ____
22. ____

Structure

5. ____
14. ____
23. ____

Rewards

6. ____
15. ____
24. ____

Strategy-Structure

Gradual Process

7. ____
16. ____
25. ____

Radical Process

8. ____
17. ____
26. ____

Learning Process

9. ____
18. ____
27. ____

Scoring Your Responses to Part 2

In the spaces next to the items on the following page, please transfer the numbers you circled on Part 2 of this instrument. You'll find it easiest to transfer your five responses (A to E) for each item—starting with item Number 28 and then ending with item Number 36. It's essential that you transfer every number accurately.

Next, separately add up each of the 5 columns, which results in **5 SUMS** (across culture, skills, teams, strategy, structure, etc.), which reveals your typical conflict-handling behavior whenever you experience any systems conflict in your group or organization. These SUMS thus constitute your Part 2 scores for your relative use of the 5 conflict modes.

KILMANN ORGANIZATIONAL CONFLICT INSTRUMENT

SYSTEMS CONFLICTS & THE FIVE CONFLICT-HANDLING MODES

Systems	Avoiding	Accommodating	Collaborating	Compromising	Competing
Culture:	28. A ___	28. B ___	28. C ___	28. D ___	28. E ___
Skills:	29. A ___	29. B ___	29. C ___	29. D ___	29. E ___
Teams:	30. A ___	30. B ___	30. C ___	30. D ___	30. E ___
Strategy:	31. A ___	31. B ___	31. C ___	31. D ___	31. E ___
Structure:	32. A ___	32. B ___	32. C ___	32. D ___	32. E ___
Rewards:	33. A ___	33. B ___	33. C ___	33. D ___	33. E ___
G-Process:	34. A ___	34. B ___	34. C ___	34. D ___	34. E ___
R-Process:	35. A ___	35. B ___	35. C ___	35. D ___	35. E ___
L-Process:	36. A ___	36. B ___	36. C ___	36. D ___	36. E ___
	SUM	SUM	SUM	SUM	SUM

Graphing Your Scores from Part 1

On page 19, you displayed your nine SUMS for those systems conflicts, as well as the average (combined) score for strategy-structure. It will now be illuminating for you to see these results on one diagram, so you can quickly identify which kinds of systems conflicts are generating negative experiences: **(H) frequently, (M) occasionally, or (L) rarely.** Using these three key distinctions will enable your group or organization to resolve its various systems conflicts, based on their priority: High (H), Medium (M), and Low (L), respectively. As you'll see, there are EIGHT TRACKS, change initiatives, which, if implemented successfully, can transform a sluggish bureaucratic organization into a vibrant quantum organization.

The first three tracks (culture, skills, and teams) represent the **informal systems:** the unwritten behavioral norms, members' styles and skills for managing people and problems, and the typical way of conducting team meetings. The next two tracks (strategy-structure and the reward system) address the **formal systems** in an organization: the officially documented mission and direction of the organization, the allocation of authority and other resources to achieve that mission, and what members are likely to receive for their performance and behavior. The last three tracks (gradual process, radical process, and learning process improvement) consider all the **processes** that flow within—and across—all the formal and informal systems in the organization, which includes how knowledge is created, stored, retrieved, and applied to improve the speed and quality by which the organization provides its products and services to its end customers and other key stakeholders. This series of eight tracks can thus renew and align all the systems and processes in an organization, which powerfully affect its internal and external stakeholders.

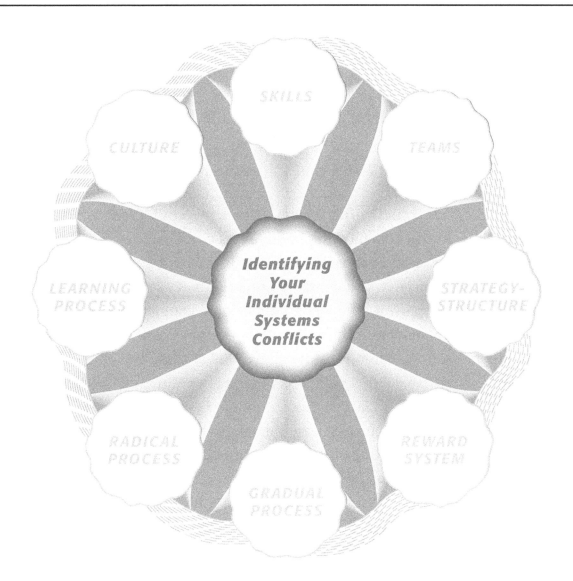

Once you've placed all your scores from page 19 onto the above diagram (which includes your average score for strategy-structure), if any score is between **3 and 6** on a systems conflict, enter L for Low. If your score is between **7 and 11,** enter M for Medium. And if your score is between **12 and 15,** enter H for High. For the sake of clarity, *use this notation for the above graph:* **4 = L, 10 = M, 14 = H,** etc.

Graphing Your Scores from Part 2

On page 21, you displayed your five SUMS for the five conflict modes. It will now be most helpful to graph your results on one diagram, so you can quickly identify your behavioral preferences for addressing the systems conflicts in your group or organization.

The Thomas-Kilmann Conflict Model defines five conflict modes, based on two underlying dimensions: assertiveness and cooperativeness. The first dimension, **assertiveness,** is the extent to which you try to satisfy *your* needs or concerns whenever you find that your wishes differ from those of another person. The second dimension, **cooperativeness,** is the extent to which you try to satisfy the *other person's* needs or concerns in a conflict situation. The various combinations of these two dimensions then define the five conflict modes: competing (high in assertiveness and low in cooperativeness), accommodating (low in assertiveness and high in cooperativeness), compromising (moderate in both assertiveness and cooperativeness), avoiding (low on both dimensions), and collaborating (high on both dimensions). Usually, people prefer to rely on only one or two of these modes, while they tend not to use the other conflict modes. But all five modes are available to a person at any time, and each mode can be every effective if it matches the key attributes of the situation. In a little while, more will be presented about when—and how—to use each conflict mode for your most troublesome systems conflicts.

For the original discussion on what became known as the TKI Conflict Model, see: Thomas, K. W., "Conflict and Conflict Management," in M. D. Dunnette (Ed.), *Handbook of Industrial and Organizational Psychology* (Chicago: Rand-McNally, 1976), 889-935.

KILMANN ORGANIZATIONAL CONFLICT INSTRUMENT

Your Individual Scores

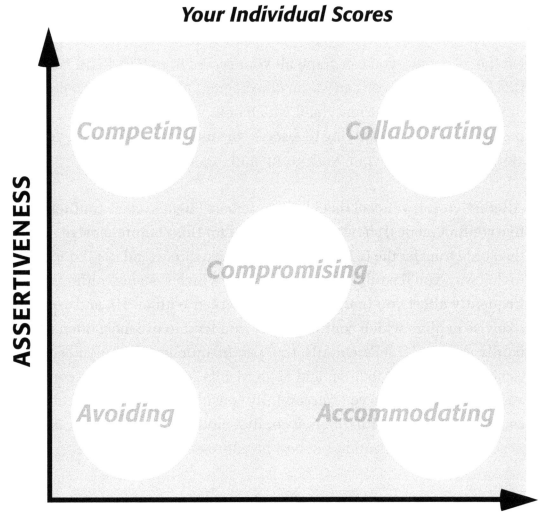

ASSERTIVENESS

Competing

Collaborating

Compromising

Avoiding

Accommodating

COOPERATIVENESS

From page 21, enter each of your five SUMS in the relevant circle inside the TKI Conflict Model. **After each score, place an L, M, or H next to the number, based on these ranges:** If your score is between **9 and 18** on any conflict mode, enter L for Low. If your score is between **19 and 35,** enter M for Medium. And if your score is between **36 and 45,** enter H for High. Again, use this notation in the TKI circles: **11 = L, 27 = M, 41 = H,** etc.

Combining Your Scores from Part 1 and Part 2

On the next page, you can graph all your scores from Part 1 and Part 2 of this instrument, so you can see on one diagram, which particular conflict modes you tend to use most (and which ones you tend to use least) in the process of addressing (trying to resolve) the most frequently experienced systems conflicts in your work group and organization.

Alternatively, if you feel that all the numbers (eight system conflicts and five conflict modes) show too much detail for this comprehensive graph, then only transfer the L, M, or H for each open circle (and not the scores). In this way, you'll be able to easily focus on which systems conflicts most frequently affect you (particular when marked with an H), and you can likewise explore which conflict modes you tend to use most often (H) or hardly use at all (L). Essentially, the specific numbers are only needed to establish the Low, Medium, and High results for your systems conflicts and conflict modes, so you can carefully consider which systems conflicts can be approached with *different* conflict modes—so your needs and the needs of your organization can best be addressed and resolved.

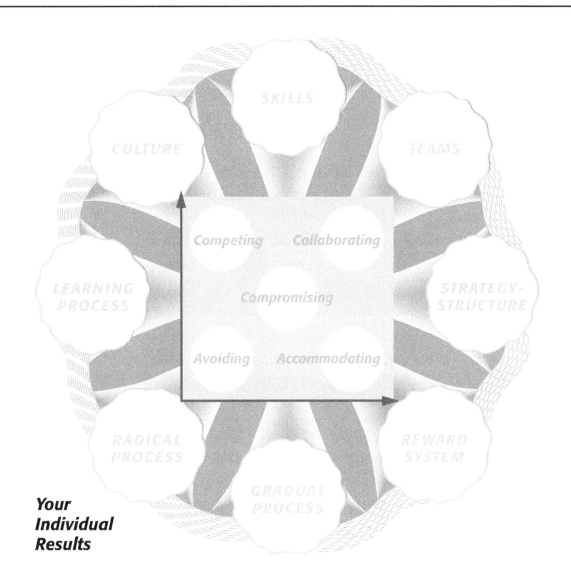

**Your
Individual
Results**

For your **systems conflicts,** transfer the eight scores that you entered on page 23 (including your average strategy-structure score) and make sure to include the L, M, or H designation after each score. For your **conflict modes,** transfer the five scores that you entered on page 25, including the L, M, or H designation after each score.

Interpreting Your Results

There are nine **systems conflicts** that conveniently sort into the eight tracks for quantum transformation (combing strategy and structure into one track). By implementing the integrated, orchestrated sequence of these eight tracks (culture, skills, teams, strategy-structure, reward systems, gradual process, radical process, and the learning process track), *your most nagging systems conflicts can first be identified and then resolved by making good use of five conflict modes* (competing, collaborating, compromising, avoiding, and accommodating). As a result of going through the eight tracks, all members will thus be able to achieve high performance and satisfaction, which will create and sustain long-term organizational success. But before more is said about quantum transformation, let's consider how to interpret your results on this instrument—so you and other members in your organization can proceed to resolve your most challenging systems conflicts.

On the following page, you can review the results for one individual: The numerical scores for the systems conflicts are placed in the outer ring of the diagram, just as you were asked to do for your own scores, including which ones are H, M, and L, as based on those ranges for High, Medium, and Low, respectively (which were defined when you graphed your own results on pages 23 and 25 of this instrument).

As you can see, there are three systems conflicts that scored in the **HIGH** range, which suggests that the member is *frequently* being hampered by negative experiences with the **culture** of her organization or group, the way in which her **team's** meetings are being conducted, and the lack of clarity and alignment in **strategy-structure.** *The three high scores suggest some very serious barriers to organizational success.*

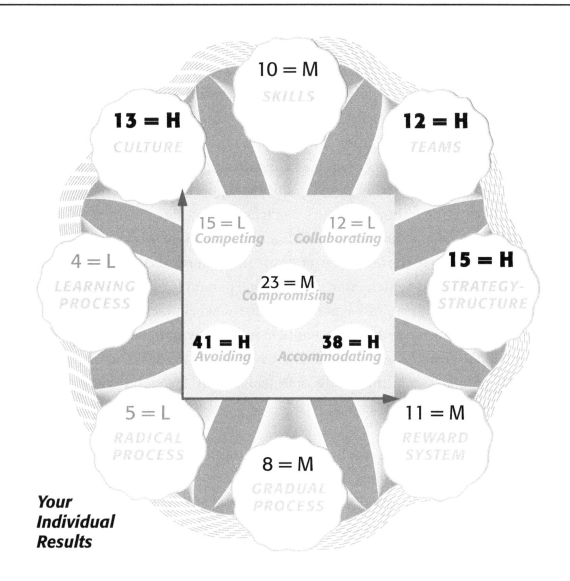

Your Individual Results

Three other conflicts (noted by the M) are *occasionally* interfering with the person's performance and satisfaction: skills, the reward system, and the processes that flow within her group. Yet two systems conflicts are LOW in their impact: radical process and learning process improvement. In all likelihood, not until those earlier conflicts are resolved will the last two process tracks become seen as key drivers of organizational success.

On the previous diagram, you can also see the person's results on the TKI Conflict Model, which shows that the low assertive modes (avoiding and accommodating) are in the **HIGH** range. As a result, this person is almost always (daily) being negatively affected by cultural norms that pressure members: (1) to remain quiet, not to express different points of view, and not to disagree with the boss (i.e., to *avoid* such conflicts); or (2) to defer to the experience of *other* members or managers (i.e., to accommodate) when discussing important issues, such as making significant changes to the formal systems, including how the reward system works in practice, and so on. Indeed, the assertive modes (competing and collaborating) are in the **LOW** range, which confirms that this person is not bringing all her talent, wisdom, ideas, and experience into the workplace. However, once the eight tracks are underway, members will be given the chance to learn more about how and when to use the five conflict modes, and especially how to *change* the culture, skills, and teams so all five modes are always available to all members—and will be used effectively as needed.

On the following page, you'll see another graph of systems conflicts and conflict modes. This time, as introduced earlier, only the H, M, and L are displayed—which makes it easy to immediately focus on the key issues: These results suggest that the integrated program of eight tracks has been proceeding—since the culture, skills, and teams are no longer frequently distracting the member (although more skill development might still be needed). Progress is also occurring for strategy-structure and the reward system, which sets the stage for resolving the conflicts in the last three process tracks of quantum transformation: After the formal systems have been revitalized, attention will then be directed to improving the speed and quality of the business and learning processes that flow within—and across—all the systems in the organization.

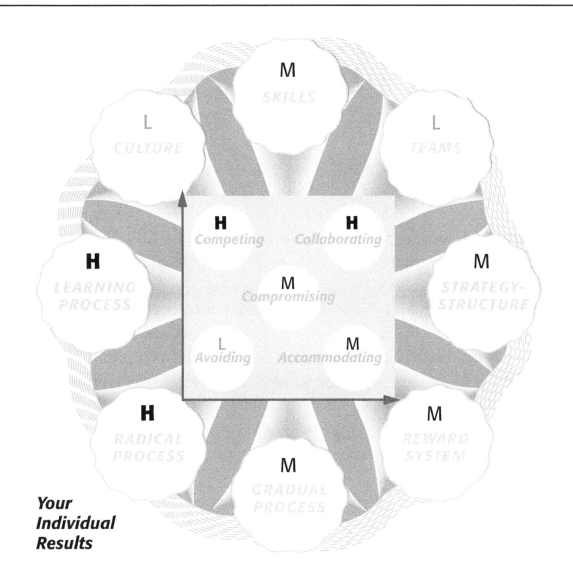

**Your
Individual
Results**

On the above graph, you can also see and analyze the results for the TKI Conflict Model: The assertive modes are **HIGH** while avoiding is **LOW,** so the "pendulum" has swung from *unassertive* (from the prior graph) to highly assertive (competing and collaborating). Usually, before the results display a balanced TKI profile (mostly medium scores), members go from the extreme use of a few modes to the extreme use of the other modes!

The graph on the next page displays the key results for a twelve-member group in a large organization. Such a graph can be developed by simply calculating the average scores of group members for each of their systems conflicts as well as for their conflict modes.

As can be seen, there are four systems conflicts, marked by an **H,** which reveal what has been negatively affecting the group members ***frequently:*** (1) culture and skills in the informal systems, (2) strategy-structure in the formal systems, and (3) processes that mostly take place inside the group (gradual process improvement). These HIGH systems conflicts across all three categories (informal systems, formal systems, and processes) shows that this work group is facing an assortment of barriers to performance and satisfaction, which severely undermines what members can provide to their organization. Moreover, the remaining systems conflicts (teams, reward systems, radical process, and learning process improvement) are ***occasionally*** interfering with performance and satisfaction. Note: There are no systems conflicts that are *rarely* affecting this group. Every conflict is negatively affecting members either frequently or occasionally.

The results on the TKI Conflict Model suggest that these group members are heavily relying on competing and accommodating for resolving their systems conflicts (HIGH), which means that members either get their own needs met...or they do their best to get the needs of *other* members in their group met. Yet there is little compromising, whereby each person gets at least some of their needs met. Indeed, the collaborating mode isn't being used much at all, so members aren't taking the necessary time to derive creative solutions to their various systems conflicts—which would help them get *their* needs met, while also helping the organization achieve *its* long-term survival and success.

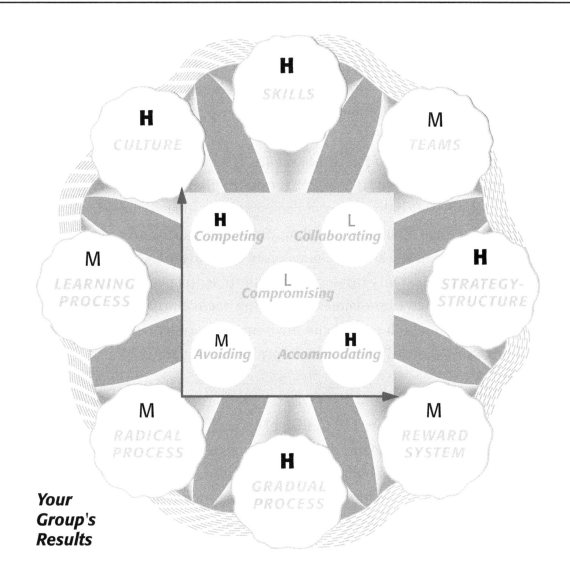

Your Group's Results

As seen on the TKI Conflict Model, the avoiding mode is being used more often than compromising and collaborating, but still less than competing or accommodating. During the program of eight tracks, especially during the culture, skills, and team tracks, group members will find it useful to discuss if their informal systems discourage them from exploring certain topics, even though they're being negatively affected by those conflicts.

On the following page is another graph of systems conflicts and conflict modes, which will help you learn how to interpret your scores as well as suggest what's possible when your work group or organization addresses its systems conflicts through the eight tracks of quantum transformation.

As you can see, *none of the eight systems conflicts have been negatively affecting the members of this organization frequently.* Rather, five system conflicts are **rarely** being experienced negatively, if at all, which suggests that members can spend most of their time contributing all their wisdom and experience to the strategic mission of their organization—surely, an excellent outcome. Only three systems conflicts (teams, reward systems, and radical process improvement) are being **occasionally** experienced in a negative way, which reveals the few remaining organizational systems and processes that still need to be improved or transformed.

Based on the success of the first three tracks, there are predictable changes that have occurred on the TKI Conflict Model: The collaborating mode is often used to resolve systems conflicts, which results in creative solutions that satisfy the needs of both internal and external stakeholders. Three of the other modes (competing, accommodating, avoiding) are being used moderately, while organizational members are not making much use of the compromising mode. Perhaps in the spirit of openly discussing their systems conflicts in depth (due to the program of eight tracks), members might be missing opportunities to choose a workable compromise when the issue is not crucial for success, and thus more time could be spend on resolving their other, more important aspects of various conflicts. As mentioned before, as the transformation proceeds, members tend to use some modes to the extreme, before they develop a more balanced use of all five modes, depending on the key attributes of the situation.

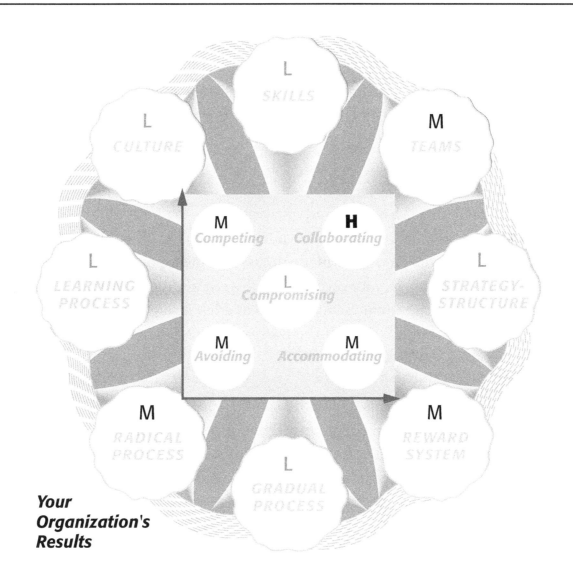

Your Organization's Results

After members retake the Organizational Conflict Instrument (e.g., every six months), they can determine their progress in addressing their systems conflicts, as the culture, skills, and team tracks help produce only low or medium scores—while those previous high scores disappear. Meanwhile, by retaking the instrument, members can see if their conflict modes are all being used more moderately, as the situation requires.

Using the Five Conflict Modes to Resolve Systems Conflicts

To fully appreciate how the five conflict modes can be used for resolving the systems conflicts that were identified by the Kilmann Organizational Conflict Instrument, let's first review the detailed definitions and use of each of the five modes:

1. **Competing** is assertive and uncooperative—an individual pursues his own concerns at the other person's expense. This is a power-oriented mode in which you use whatever power seems appropriate to win your own position—your ability to argue, your rank, or economic sanctions. Competing means "standing up for your rights," defending a position which you believe is correct, or simply trying to win.

2. **Accommodating** is unassertive and cooperative—the complete opposite of competing. When accommodating, the individual neglects his own concerns to satisfy the concerns of the other person; there is an element of self-sacrifice in this mode. Accommodating might take the form of selfless generosity or charity, obeying another person's order when you would prefer not to, or yielding to another's point of view.

3. **Avoiding** is unassertive and uncooperative—the person neither pursues his own concerns nor those of the other individual. Thus he does not deal with the conflict. Avoiding might take the form of diplomatically sidestepping an issue, postponing an issue until a better time, or simply withdrawing from a threatening situation.

4. **Collaborating** is both assertive and cooperative—the complete opposite of avoiding. Collaborating involves an attempt to work with others to find some solution that fully satisfies their concerns. It means digging into an issue to pinpoint the underlying needs and wants of the two individuals. Collaborating between two persons might take the form of exploring a disagreement to learn from each other's insights or trying to find a creative solution to an interpersonal problem.

5. **Compromising** is moderate in both assertiveness and cooperativeness. The objective is to find some expedient, mutually acceptable solution that partially satisfies both parties. It falls intermediate between competing and accommodating. Compromising gives up more than competing but less than accommodating. Likewise, it addresses an issue more directly than avoiding, but does not explore it in as much depth as collaborating. In some situations, compromising might mean splitting the difference between the two positions, exchanging concessions, or seeking a quick middle-ground solution.

Each of us is capable of using all five conflict-handling modes. But certain people use some modes more and better than others, whether because of temperament or habit. But remember this first key principle: ***About 80% of what takes place in an organization is determined by its systems and processes, while 20% is determined by member desires or preferences.*** This principle provides THE rationale for taking this instrument, so you can identify (1) your surrounding systems conflicts and (2) your relative use of the five conflict modes—which will then enable you (with various change initiatives) to resolve those conflicts and thus achieve success.

Here's the second key principle to keep in mind (which follows directly from the first principle): ***Choose the particular conflict-handling mode that best matches the key attributes of the situation.*** Therefore, don't use any conflict mode out of habit or based only on your typical preferences. Instead, choose—and use—one or more of the five conflict modes based exclusively on how you would answer these fundamental questions:

The Eight Key Attributes of a Conflict Situation
1. **Is there overwhelming stress?**
2. **Is the conflict simple or complex?**
3. **How important is the topic to each person in the situation?**
4. **Is there time to discuss the issues?**
5. **Is there sufficient trust to openly share needs and concerns?**
6. **Do people have good listening and communication skills?**
7. **Does the culture and reward system actively encourage people to share their true needs and concerns?**
8. **How important are relationships to each person in the situation?**

Depending on these eight attributes, members choose the conflict mode that has the best chance of satisfying their most important needs, plus the most important needs of their organization and its key stakeholders.

Of course, members must develop (and continually enhance) their skills for correctly reading the key attributes of any conflict situation. And then they must practice using some of their infrequently used conflict modes, while also consciously reducing the overuse of their other modes. But to reemphasize the key point: The first step for managing conflict is reading the immediate situation *before* selecting a mode of behavior, so members and the organization can get their most important needs met.

KILMANN ORGANIZATIONAL CONFLICT INSTRUMENT

Below are five listings for when it is best to use each of the five conflict modes, depending on the particular quality and nature of the eight key attributes of a conflict situation. Note: Each numbered item on these lists (1, 2, 3, etc.) corresponds to the same numbered attribute that appears on the previous page. Naturally, you and your group members must have the opportunity to practice reading several conflict situations and then select the best mode to use in each situation. Practice, practice, practice....

When to Use Competing
1. Stress is high or moderate
2. Problem is simple: unidimensional
3. Problem is more important to you than to others
4. There is little time for discussion
5. Low or moderate levels of trust exist
6. People can communicate their views
7. The culture and reward system support members who argue their positions in a win/lose manner
8. People are not concerned with sustaining their relationships

When to Use Collaborating
1. Stress is stimulating
2. Problem is complex: multidimensional
3. Problem is equally important to all
4. There is much time for discussion
5. High levels of trust exist
6. Interactions are effective
7. The culture and the reward system actively encourage exploration, cooperation, and teamwork
8. People want their relationships to improve—and last

When to Use Compromising

1. Stress is high or moderate
2. Problem is simple: unidimensional
3. Problem is moderately important to all
4. There is little time for discussion
5. Moderate or low levels of trust exist
6. Interactions are respectful
7. The culture and reward system encourage quick fixes
8. People are indifferent about their relationships

When to Use Avoiding

1. Stress is overwhelming
2. Problem is simple: unidimensional
3. Problem is not important
4. There is little time for discussion
5. Low levels of trust exist
6. Interactions are ineffective
7. The culture and reward system discourage confrontation
8. People don't particularly care about their relationships

When to Use Accommodating

1. Stress is moderate or high
2. Problem is simple: unidimensional
3. Problem is more important to others
4. There is little time for discussion
5. Moderate or low levels of trust exist
6. Interactions are ineffective
7. The culture and reward system encourage compliance
8. People are eager to please others to maintain their relationships

After members have had several opportunities to read conflict situations and then practice enacting one or more conflict modes that seem to best match the key attributes of each situation, members still want to know the best approach to use whenever they're ready to address (and resolve) their most challenging systems conflicts:

The Best Approach to Conflict Management

- **Know that you have all five conflict modes available to you at all times, in all situations**
- **Develop the ability to read (assess) the eight key attributes of any conflict situation**
- **Choose the conflict mode that best fits the specific situation**
- **Enact the chosen mode with care, sensitivity, and respect**
- **Switch to a different conflict mode as you experience changes in the key attributes of the situation**
- **Continue to improve your listening and communication skills— and your ability to engender trust**

It is during the second track of quantum transformation, the skills track, when members learn about people management, problem management, time management, and conflict management. All these skills are needed whenever members seek to address their systems conflicts and any other conflicts that emerge in the workplace. Moreover, even before these skills can be further enhanced for the benefit of the membership as well as the organization, the culture must actively encourage this essential learning process, which must also be assessed through the performance appraisal system. Therefore, a complete program of quantum transformation must be implemented not only to prepare members for approaching their work in new ways, but also to resolve their most challenging systems conflicts.

Implementing the Eight Tracks to Resolve Systems Conflicts

Here is the third key principle to remember at all times: *In the short term, the organization's systems and processes are fixed, so the use of one or more conflict modes might be significantly constrained by the nature and quality of the key attributes of the situation—as dictated by those particular systems and processes. But in the long term, those systems and processes (which determine "the situation" for conflict resolution) can be transformed, which then changes the eight key attributes of any conflict situation to support the use of all five modes, as needed.*

This third key principle reminds us that the collaborating mode—which is essential for resolving systems conflicts in a manner that satisfies the needs and concerns of all internal and external stakeholders—can only work successfully when the key attributes of the situation support using the collaborating mode, such as stimulating (not overwhelming) stress, high levels of trust among members, sufficient time to address the topic, and so forth. (See page 39 for a list of the eight key attributes that support the collaborating mode). But if the current systems and processes do *not* support the collaborating mode (and, in fact, primarily support using the avoiding or compromising mode), then members, in the short term, won't be able to use the collaborating mode to resolve their systems conflicts— nor will members be able to collaborate successfully on any of their *other* technical, business, and management conflicts.

In the long run, however, the organization can transform its systems and processes to support the use of the collaborating mode (as well as all the other conflict modes) to resolve not only any lingering systems conflicts, but also to resolve any of their other complex conflicts and challenges.

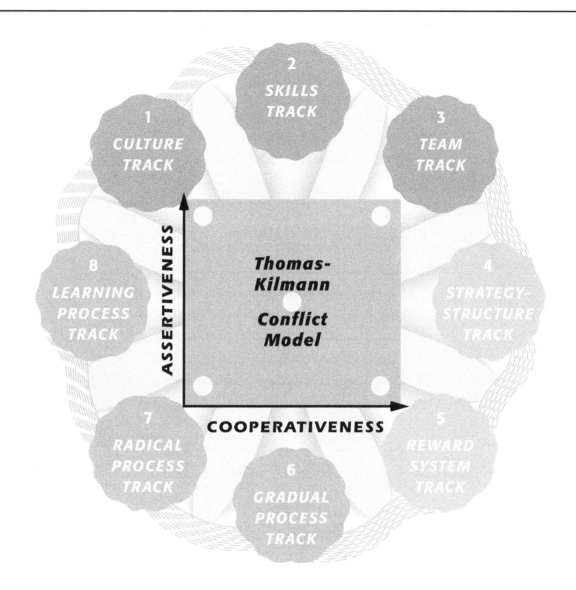

This diagram shows the integrated sequence of eight tracks, which, with the increasing use of all five conflict modes (as the systems and processes are revitalized and aligned for the future), will enable the organization to utilize all the wisdom, knowledge, talent, and experience of its members, no matter what the topic or focus of discussion happens to be.

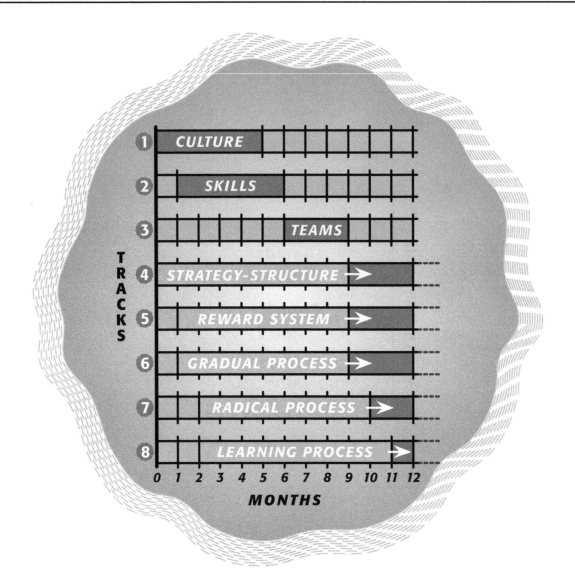

After the organization has made significant progress implementing the eight tracks of quantum transformation, members will be able to read the situation that surrounds any subject and then choose the conflict mode(s) that best fit with the key attributes of that particular situation. For more information about the eight tracks, visit **www.kilmanndiagnostics.com** or read Dr. Ralph H. Kilmann's 2011 book, ***Quantum Organizations.***

Online Products by Kilmann Diagnostics
www.kilmanndiagnostics.com

Online Courses

00. Expanding Consciousness Course

0. Quantum Transformation Course

1. BASIC Training in Conflict Management

2. GROUP Training in Conflict Management

3. ADVANCED Training in Conflict Management

4. Culture Management Course

5. Critical Thinking Course

6. Team Management Course

7. Strategy-Structure Course

8. Reward Systems Course

9. Process Management Course

Online Course Collections

10. The Complete Program of ALL Courses

11. The TKI Package of Three Courses

Online Assessment Tools

Thomas-Kilmann Conflict Mode Instrument (TKI)

Kilmann-Saxton Culture-Gap® Survey

Organizational Courage Assessment

Kilmann Organizational Conflict Instrument (KOCI)

Publications by Kilmann Diagnostics

Self-Report Assessment Tools

Kilmann-Saxton Culture-Gap® Survey

Kilmanns Organizational Belief Survey

Kilmanns Time-Gap Survey

Kilmanns Team-Gap Survey

Organizational Courage Assessment

Kilmann-Covin Organizational Influence Survey

Kilmanns Personality Style Instrument

Kilmann Organizational Conflict Instrument (KOCI)

The Book That Explains the Eight Tracks

Quantum Organizations

Materials for Implementing the Eight Tracks

Work Sheets for Identifying and Closing Culture-Gaps

Work Sheets for Identifying and Closing Team-Gaps

Consultant Schedules for Implementing the Tracks

Logisitics Manual for Implementing the Tracks

Workbooks for Implementing the Tracks

The Book for Expanding Consciousness

The Courageous Mosaic

CPSIA information can be obtained
at www.ICGtesting.com
Printed in the USA
LVHW060623250123
737854LV00008B/836